DRUM ALONG

10 CLASSIC ROCK SONGS ★ JØRG FABIG

COLDPLAY, BRYAN ADAMS, THE BEATLES, THE POLICE and more

CW00409457

WISE PUBLICATIONS
part of The Music Sales Group

London / New York / Paris / Sydney / Copenhagen / Berlin / Madrid / Tokyo

Published by
Wise Publications
14-15 Berners Street, London, W1T 3LJ, UK.

Exclusive distributors:
Music Sales Limited
Distribution Centre, Newmarket Road,
Bury St Edmunds, Suffolk, IP33 3YB, UK.

Music Sales Pty Limited
120 Rothschild Avenue, Rosebery, NSW 2018, Australia.

Order No. AM993586
ISBN 978-1-84772-550-9
This book © Copyright 2007 Wise Publications,
a division of Music Sales Limited.

Unauthorised reproduction of any part
of this publication by any means including
photocopying is an infringement of copyright.

Printed in the EU.

www.musicsales.com

PREFACE 4

LEAD SHEETS 5

HOW TO PRACTISE 6

OASIS ★ SUPERSONIC 8

THE BEATLES ★ LET IT BE 10

OTIS REDDING ★ (SITTIN' ON) THE DOCK OF THE BAY 18

THE POLICE ★ EVERY BREATH YOU TAKE 12

BRYAN ADAMS ★ SUMMER OF '69 14

REAMONN ★ SUPERGIRL 20

THE CURE ★ FRIDAY I'M IN LOVE 22

COLDPLAY ★ CLOCKS 24

TOM PETTY & THE HEARTBREAKERS ★ FREE FALLIN' 26

SYSTEM OF A DOWN ★ LONELY DAY 28

EXPLANATION OF NOTATION 31

CD TRACK LISTING 32

PREFACE

To play the drums in a rock band is the aim of lots of young drummers. This book is intended to help you achieve this goal. The drummer in a band is responsible for a steady and solid beat. According to technical and musical abilities there is need for plenty of rehearsing – but how, without guitar, bass and keyboard? What are the most important aspects of good drumming?

The written parts to the songs in this book are devised as lead sheets; you will get to know what this means later. It is not the idea of this book to transcribe the original drum parts measure by measure and practise them note by note. For this it would need volumes of music and lots of practising time. The method used in this book should help the beginner drummer to play well-known rock songs with simple grooves, easily and quickly.

The CD contains recordings of these songs, done with vocals, guitar, bass, keyboard and drums. If possible you should convert these play-alongs into mp3-files using a PC. With an mp3-player on your PC, you can play them in different tempos without changing the pitch. This is quite important, since you should play the parts very slowly at the beginning and accelerate the tempo later, when you feel comfortable with the song you are working on. Of course, there is also a track without drums, so at last you can play along with the 'band'.

Enjoy working with this book – I wish you lots of success!

EXPLANATION OF THE LEAD SHEETS

Rock songs consist of different parts, which are usually repeated several times during a song. The most important parts are 'verse' and 'chorus', as well as the 'intro', 'outro' and instrumental solo parts. 'Bridge' is the name for a part which connects to more important parts where there is a vocal line in the original, an 'interlude' divides parts without a vocal line; if there is a very significant instrumental line in an interlude it is called a 'riff'.

It is very important for the drummer to hear the structure of a rock song. Each part is played with a different pattern, for example you change between hi-hat and ride cymbal, or the chorus is played with eight notes on the hi-hat, the bridge with quarter notes. During one part you usually use the same pattern, which can consist of one or more measures. Sometimes, one pattern fits a whole song.

The songs in this book are notated as lead sheets. Each part of the song is written in a single line. On the left you have the number of bars, the length of a song part. If the time signature is not stated on the top of the sheet, it will be in 4/4 time. In the middle of the page there is the name of the song part (verse, chorus, bridge, intro, outro, etc.). On the right-hand side you will find the drum pattern to the part. Important: If it is a pattern with more measures than one, you will have to watch the number of repeats. An example: The verse of a song is 16 bars long, you have a four-measure pattern to this part. In this case the pattern needs to be repeated four times.

Sometimes the same part is played with a different pattern, when repeated. In this case the parts are named e.g. 'verse A', 'verse B', 'verse C'. It might be that in a song there is possibly also 'chorus A', then 'chorus B', and then 'chorus A' again. The pattern played with 'chorus A' is always the same.

In some parts of a song there may be 'stops'. This means that the pattern to this part is repeated a number of times, and then stops on a determined beat – after this, there are no drums at all. 'Stop in bar 7 on beat 3' means that you repeat a one-measure pattern six times completely, and in the seventh bar you stop the pattern on beat 3, e.g. with a bass drum beat. If this part of the song is eight bars long, the end of bar seven and the whole eighth bar remain without the drums being played.

Lots of songs end with 'repeat and fade out'. Repeat the last pattern of the song as long as you can still hear the other instruments playing and try to play softer and softer as you go along. All of this sounds very sophisticated, but if you simply read the lead sheets while listening to the music, you will find out that it is quite easy. The song parts of the recordings on the CD are absolutely identical to the parts of the original songs. I warmly recommend listening to the original recordings, while reading the lead sheets. This will give you an idea of the style and sound of the original music.

HOW TO PRACTISE

First of all you need to work out all of the patterns that belong to one song very carefully until you are really comfortable with them. During lessons, your teacher could call out the name of a song part while you play, then count one bar, and you change to the new part he called for. The next step is to listen to the song while reading the lead sheets and paying attention to the song's structure.

Can you recognise the transition of the parts, are there significant guitar lines, is the vocal line going up or down etc.? As soon as you feel comfortable, you should listen to the song once more and mark every new part, e.g. with a crash cymbal on beat 1.

Now you should start to play with the song, starting slowly. Use an mp3-player on your computer to reduce the tempo without changing the pitch. Count and listen to each part of the song, so you can always play the correct pattern to each part.

Of course the drummers on the original recordings play a lot more than is notated in this book. If you feel comfortable with the song, you can start playing fill-ins at the ends of the different parts, playing variations of the patterns, hi-hat openings etc. Listen carefully to the original recordings and let them inspire you. But never forget that it is most important to keep the tempo and to be sure in which part of the song you are – safety first! This is even more important when playing together with other instrumentalists.

Special suggestions for group education

If your lesson is a group lesson, there are lots of possibilities to work out the songs:

• drums only: one student starts with a certain pattern, the other listens, calls out a new part, counts to four and takes over. The first one stops, listens and calls out a new part, etc.

• with music: one student plays the patterns, the other one marks every new song part with a crash cymbal on beat 1 of the new part.

• the students alternate between the song parts: the first one starts with the first part, the second one takes over with the next, etc.

• If there are stops in a song: the first student plays until the first stop, the second takes over, etc.

Remember the following points when rehearsing with a band:

• Always start very slowly.

• Rehearse every part of the song separately.

• Give a lot of attention to the connections of song parts, e.g. play the last four bars of the verse and the first four bars of the following chorus directly afterwards. Repeat this several times.

• Make sure that you know which part to rehearse first and don't stop playing just because of one wrong note somewhere.

• When you have worked out the song at a slow tempo you can play it a little bit faster.

• Before performing the song on stage you should have lots of run-throughs. Don't stop for every mistake, always try to go on. This is quite important, because on stage things will happen anyway. Mistakes are common in music, nobody's perfect! Even the big stars make mistakes on stage – if they don't let you know, you will never find out.

SUPERSONIC

Words & Music by Noel Gallagher

OASIS

♩ = 105

4 **INTRO 1**

DRUMS SOLO

8 **INTRO 2**
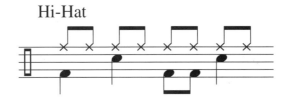

16 **VERSE**

8 **BRIDGE**

16 **CHORUS AND RIFF**

© COPYRIGHT 1994 OASIS MUSIC/CREATION SONGS LIMITED.
SONY/ATV MUSIC PUBLISHING (UK) LIMITED.
ALL RIGHTS RESERVED. INTERNATIONAL COPYRIGHT SECURED.

4   **INTERLUDE**

16   **VERSE**

8   **BRIDGE**

16   **CHORUS AND RIFF**

4   **RIFF/OUTRO**

REPEAT AND FADE OUT

Let it Be

Words & Music by John Lennon & Paul McCartney

THE BEATLES

♩ = 72

4 **INTRO** *NO DRUMS*

8 **VERSE A** *NO DRUMS*

4 **CHORUS A** *NO DRUMS*

8 **VERSE B**

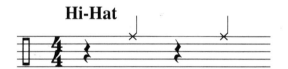

8 **CHORUS B**

© COPYRIGHT 1970 NORTHERN SONGS.
ALL RIGHTS RESERVED. INTERNATIONAL COPYRIGHT SECURED.

4   **INTERLUDE**

8   **GUITAR SOLO**

4   **CHORUS C**

8   **VERSE C**

8   **CHORUS C**

2   **OUTRO**

every breath you take

Words & Music by Sting

THE POLICE

♩ = 118

8 INTRO

16 VERSE A

8 CHORUS

8 VERSE B

10 BRIDGE

© COPYRIGHT 1983 MAGNETIC PUBLISHING LIMITED/EMI MUSIC PUBLISHING LIMITED.
ALL RIGHTS RESERVED. INTERNATIONAL COPYRIGHT SECURED.

16   **INTERLUDE**

8   **CHORUS**

14   **VERSE B**

4   **OUTRO A**

8   **OUTRO B**    *REPEAT AND FADE OUT*

SUMMER OF '69

Words & Music by Bryan Adams & Jim Vallance

BRYAN ADAMS

♩ = 139

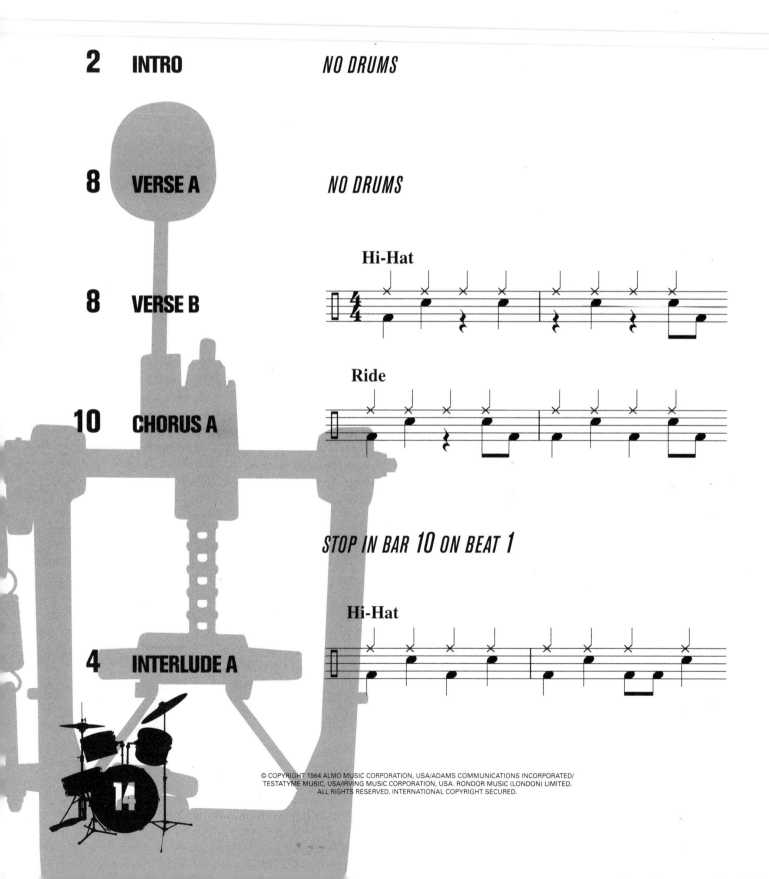

2 INTRO — *NO DRUMS*

8 VERSE A — *NO DRUMS*

8 VERSE B — Hi-Hat

10 CHORUS A — Ride

STOP IN BAR 10 ON BEAT 1

4 INTERLUDE A — Hi-Hat

© COPYRIGHT 1984 ALMO MUSIC CORPORATION, USA/ADAMS COMMUNICATIONS INCORPORATED/
TESTATYME MUSIC, USA/IRVING MUSIC CORPORATION, USA. RONDOR MUSIC (LONDON) LIMITED.
ALL RIGHTS RESERVED. INTERNATIONAL COPYRIGHT SECURED.

14

8   **VERSE C**

10   **CHORUS B**

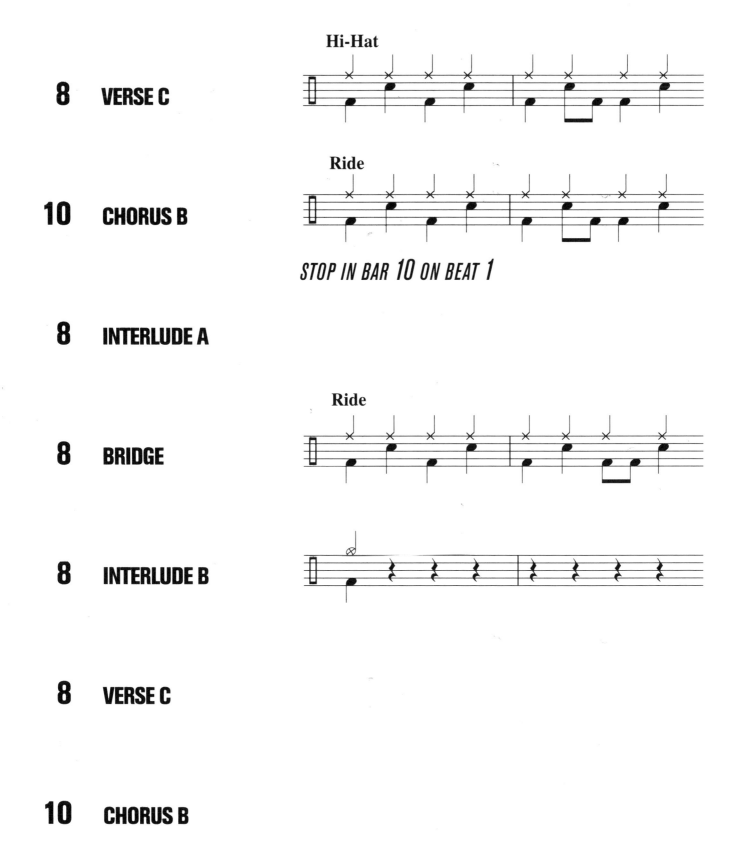

STOP IN BAR 10 ON BEAT 1

8   **INTERLUDE A**

8   **BRIDGE**

8   **INTERLUDE B**

8   **VERSE C**

10   **CHORUS B**

8   **INTERLUDE A**
       (OUTRO)   *REPEAT AND FADE OUT*

photo: Olaf Heine

(Sittin' On) THE DOCK OF THE BAY

Words & Music
by Steve Cropper
& Otis Redding

OTIS REDDING

♩ = 104

4 **INTRO**   *NO DRUMS*

8 **VERSE**

8 **CHORUS**

8 **VERSE**

8 **CHORUS**

© COPYRIGHT 1967 EAST MEMPHIS MUSIC CORPORATION/IRVING MUSIC INCORPORATED/COTILLION MUSIC INCORPORATED, USA.
RONDOR MUSIC (LONDON) LIMITED (75%)/WARNER/CHAPPELL MUSIC LIMITED (25%).
ALL RIGHTS RESERVED. INTERNATIONAL COPYRIGHT SECURED.

8   BRIDGE

8   VERSE

8   CHORUS

8   OUTRO

REPEAT AND FADE OUT

supergirl

Words & Music by Raymond Michael Garvey/
Sebastian Padotzke/Uwe Bossert/Mike Gommeringer/
Philipp Rauenbusch

REAMONN

♩ = 116

8 INTRO

16 VERSE

16 CHORUS A

16 VERSE

16 CHORUS A

© COPYRIGHT ARABELLA MUSIKVERLAG GMBH*(50%)
(BMG MUSIC PUBLISHING GERMANY), MÜNCHEN/
B612 PUBLISHING GMBH (50%).
ALL RIGHTS RESERVED. INTERNATIONAL COPYRIGHT SECURED.

8 **CHORUS B**

8 **CHORUS C**

16 **OUTRO**

1 **LAST BAR**

Friday I'm In Love

Words by Robert Smith
Music by Robert Smith, Simon Gallup,
Porl Thompson, Boris Williams
& Perry Bamonte

THE CURE

♩ = 136

16 INTRO

16 VERSE

6 CHORUS

8 VERSE

8 INTERLUDE

© COPYRIGHT FICTION SONGS LIMITED.
SVL: MUSIK-EDITION DISCOTON GMBH (BMG MUSIC PUBLISHING GERMANY), MÜNCHEN.
ALLE RECHTE FÜR DEUTSCHLAND, ÖSTERREICH, SCHWEIZ.

8 VERSE

6 CHORUS

16 BRIDGE

16 VERSE

16 OUTRO

STOP IN BAR 15 ON 4+

CLOCKS

Words & Music by Guy Berryman, Chris Martin,
Jon Buckland & Will Champion

COLDPLAY

♩ = 131

8 **INTRO 1** *NO DRUMS*

8 **INTRO 2**

16 **VERSE**

8 **CHORUS A**

8 **KEYBOARD RIFF 1**

16 **VERSE**

© COPYRIGHT 2003 BMG MUSIC PUBLISHING LIMITED.
SVL: MUSIK-EDITION DISCOTON GMBH (BMG MUSIC PUBLISHING GERMANY), MÜNCHEN.
ALLE RECHTE FÜR DEUTSCHLAND, ÖSTERREICH, SCHWEIZ.
ALL RIGHTS RESERVED. INTERNATIONAL COPYRIGHT SECURED.

24

16   **CHORUS A**

16   **KEYBOARD RIFF 2**

16   **BRIDGE**

8   **INTERLUDE**

8   **KEYBOARD RIFF 2**

8   **CHORUS B**

16   **CHORUS C**

8   **OUTRO**

free fallin'

Words & Music by Tom Petty & Jeff Lynne

TOM PETTY

♩ = 85

4 **INTRO** *NO DRUMS*

8 **VERSE A** *NO DRUMS*

2 **INTERLUDE**

8 **VERSE B**

8 **CHORUS**

© COPYRIGHT 1989 EMI APRIL MUSIC INCORPORATED, USA/GONE GATOR MUSIC, USA.
RECHTE FÜR DEUTSCHLAND, ÖSTERREICH, SCHWEIZ & OSTEUROPA (AUSSER BALTIKUM): EMI MUSIC PUBLISHING GERMANY GMBH & CO.KG (20%).
UNIVERSAL/MCA MUSICLIMITED. ALL RIGHTS IN GERMANY ADMINISTERED BY UNIVERSAL/MCA MUSIC PUBL. GMBH (80%).
ALL RIGHTS RESERVED. INTERNATIONAL COPYRIGHT SECURED.

8   **VERSE B**

8   **CHORUS**

8   **BRIDGE 1**

8   **VERSE C**

8   **CHORUS**

4   **BRIDGE 2**

8   **CHORUS**   *REPEAT AND FADE OUT*

LONELY DAY

Words & Music by Serj Tankian & Daron Malakian

SYSTEM OF A DOWN

♩. = 76

4   **INTRO 1**   *NO DRUMS*

8   **VERSE A**   *NO DRUMS*

4   **CHORUS A**

8   **VERSE B**

4   **BRIDGE A**

2   **BRIDGE B**

28

© COPYRIGHT 2005 SONY/ATV SONGS LLC/
SHATTERED MIRRORS PUBLISHING, USA/MALAKIAN PUBLISHING, USA.
SONY/ATV MUSIC PUBLISHING (UK) LIMITED.
ALL RIGHTS RESERVED. INTERNATIONAL COPYRIGHT SECURED.

8   **GUITAR SOLO**

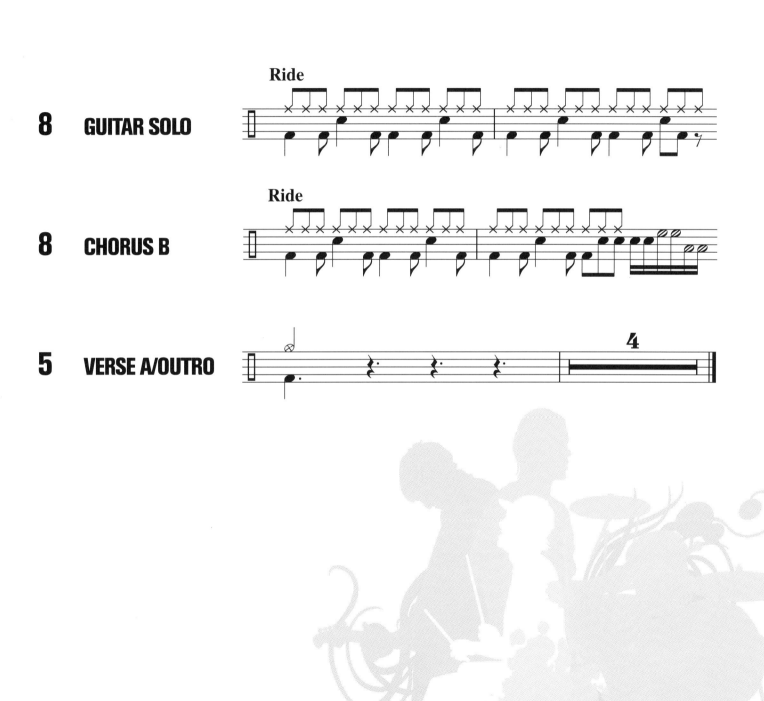

8   **CHORUS B**

5   **VERSE A/OUTRO**

EXPLANATION OF NOTATION

HI-HAT OR RIDE CYMBAL

SNARE DRUM

BASS DRUM

HIGH TOM-TOM

MID TOM-TOM

LOW TOM-TOM

CRASH CYMBAL

CD TRACK LISTING

1 **SUPERSONIC -** FULL VERSION
2 **SUPERSONIC -** CLICKTRACK
3 **LET IT BE -** FULL VERSION
4 **LET IT BE -** CLICKTRACK
5 **EVERY BREATH YOU TAKE -** FULL VERSION
6 **EVERY BREATH YOU TAKE -** CLICKTRACK
7 **SUMMER OF '69 -** FULL VERSION
8 **SUMMER OF '69 -** CLICKTRACK
9 **(SITTIN' ON) THE DOCK OF THE BAY -** FULL VERSION
10 **(SITTIN' ON) THE DOCK OF THE BAY -** CLICKTRACK
11 **SUPERGIRL -** FULL VERSION
12 **SUPERGIRL -** CLICKTRACK
13 **FRIDAY I'M IN LOVE -** FULL VERSION
14 **FRIDAY I'M IN LOVE -** CLICKTRACK
15 **CLOCKS -** FULL VERSION
16 **CLOCKS -** CLICKTRACK
17 **FREE FALLIN' -** FULL VERSION
18 **FREE FALLIN' -** CLICKTRACK
19 **LONELY DAY -** FULL VERSION
20 **LONELY DAY -** CLICKTRACK